PASSPORT READING

JOURNEYS™

WORD STUDY

Expanded Learning
Voyager

PHOTO CREDITS

p. 5 © Edwin Remsberg/Alamy; p. 9 © Organics image library/Alamy, © 2005 www.photos.com; p. 13 © BRUCE COLEMAN INC./Alamy; p. 17 © 2005 www.photos.com, © imagebroker/Alamy, © Trevor Smithers ARPS/Alamy; p. 20 © Royalty-Free/Corbis; p. 25 © Winston Fraser/Alamy; p. 29 © Jeff Schultz/AlaskaStock.com; p. 33 Renee Quintal Daily; p. 37 © Royalty-Free/Corbis; p. 40 Courtesy John Musselman/www.stlbiking.com; p. 45 John Hudgens; p. 49 © 2005 www.photos.com, © 2005 www.clipart.com; p. 53 John Hudgens; p. 57 © Realimage/Alamy; p. 60 © 2005, By Kids For Kids Co. Used By Permission/www.BKFK.com; p. 65 © Royalty-Free/Corbis; p. 69 Dillon Wardian; p. 73 © ImageDJ/Alamy; p. 77 John Hudgens; p. 80 © 2005 www.photos.com; p. 85 © Allstar Picture Library/Alamy; p. 89 City of Scottsdale Parks & Recreation; p. 93 © BananaStock/Alamy; p. 97 Jon Way/Reuters; p. 100 AP Photo/Wilfredo Lee; p. 105 © DIOMEDIA/Alamy; p. 109 © 2005 www.photos.com; p. 113 Courtesy Roadsideamerica.com; p. 117 © Nicholas Pitt/Alamy, © Rolf Richardson/Alamy; p. 120 © 2005 www.photos.com.

ISBN 13: 978-1-4168-0882-4
ISBN: 1-4168-0882-5
208127

11 12 13 14 15 WEB 9 8 7
17855 Dallas Parkway, Suite 400 • Dallas, Texas 75287 • 1-888-399-1995

Table of Contents

LESSON 1

FLUENCY Read the Independent Reading passage out loud in a small group. Read the passage a second time. Try to read each word correctly and increase your speed.

A

1. can	glad	fact	sack
2. net	men	stem	test
3. wax	tell	left	plan
4. jet	man	nest	slam

B

1. friend	grow	these	become
2. ones	mat	what	pet
3. said	bag	leg	they

C

1. _____	**4.** _____
2. _____	**5.** _____
3. _____	**6.** _____

VOCABULARY

1. _____

_____

2. _____

_____

3. _____

_____

4. _____

_____

5. _____

_____

Meg's Quest

*Meg dabbed sweat from her brow. Her **quest** for the Rafflesia, the world's largest and smelliest flower, had taken her to a rain forest.*

The Rafflesia does not have leaves, stems, or roots. It takes about nine months for its flower to open. When it does, it has five petals and can span five feet from end to end.

Meg smelled something awful. It smelled like rotting flesh. "I'm close!"

*she said. The Rafflesia is called the "corpse flower" because of its bad smell. Meg heard buzzing. She saw a group of flies. They are **attracted** to the Rafflesia's smell. Spikes in the flower hold several gallons of nectar. The flies **pollinate** the flower.*

*Meg **tracked** the smell and the flies. "Aha!" she clapped with happiness.*

Max's Test

Max has a plan to test his friends. This is what he tells them.

"The banyan tree grows up and then down," he says. "It can grow to be 100 feet tall. Roots grow from its branches back to the land. They become stems that **support** the tree. These stems can become trunks. The biggest banyan tree has 350 big trunks and more than 3,000 small ones." Max asks, "Do you think these are facts?"

A lot of his friends say no. They are wrong! What Max said are facts!

LESSON 2

FLUENCY

With a partner, read yesterday's independent passage as a play. One person is the narrator. He or she reads the first and last paragraphs. The narrator may also read the words "he says" and "Max asks" in the second paragraph. The second person reads with feeling Max's speech in paragraph 2. Then switch roles and read the passage again.

A

1.	mix	rib	mint	twig
2.	lot	box	stop	spot
3.	skin	toss	sick	rot
4.	ramp	best	step	crab

B

1.	people	some	other	have
2.	friend	span	says	test
3.	these	grow	stem	plan

C

1. _____   **4.** _____

2. _____   **5.** _____

3. _____   **6.** _____

VOCABULARY

1. compost _____

_____

2. layer _____

_____

3. medicine _____

_____

4. garlic _____

_____

Skip the Trash

You just finished eating a salad. You are heading to the trashcan to throw away what is left on your plate. STOP! Take a second look. You can use what's left to grow your own food.

*Building a **compost** pile is the first step in growing plants for food. Choose a spot for the **compost** pile. Dig up the dirt there. Build the pile in **layers**. Start with a **layer** of things that are brown and dry. This includes twigs, dry leaves, boxes, and newspapers. Next, toss on a **layer** of things that are green and wet, such as kitchen scraps, flowers, weeds, and fresh grass clippings. Your pile should be about three feet wide and three feet high. It will be ready to use in your garden in about a year.*

Plants that Help

Some plants can be used as **medicine**. Some of these plants may be in your kitchen!

A lot of people cook with **garlic**. It has other uses, too. If you get a wasp or bee sting, try this trick. Crush some **garlic** and put it on the sting.

It is easy to grow mint. You can put mint leaves in tea. You can chop them up and mix them in a salad. If you have an upset stomach, eat mint to feel better. If you have an itch, put it on your skin. The itch will stop.

LESSON 3

FLUENCY With a partner, read yesterday's independent passage as a news reporter reading a newscast. Your partner should follow along and check for reading errors. Then switch roles and read the passage again.

A

1. mud	dug	sun	tug
2. drum	jump	fuss	rub
3. weld	left	drop	grab
4. sock	cast	belt	swim

B

1. brought	touch	because	enough
2. people	friend	other	grow
3. help	have	grin	some

C

1. _____   4. _____
2. _____   5. _____
3. _____   6. _____

VOCABULARY

kudzu	profit	vine	clung

Make Lemonade...or Jelly

There is a saying you may have heard. "When life gives you lemons, make lemonade." The saying means that when something bad happens, make something good out of it. Some people are doing this with a **vine** *called* **kudzu**.

Kudzu *grows on everything. Its spreading has created quite a fuss. The* **kudzu** *vines can grow up to 60 feet in one year. It is hard to get rid of.*

Some people have made a **profit** *from* **kudzu**. *The* **vines** *are like rubber. Some people use the* **vines** *to make strong baskets. Others let goats graze on the* **vines**. *There are even people who use the buds to make jelly and syrup. When life gives you* **kudzu**, *make jelly!*

Kudzu

Kudzu comes from Japan. People brought it to the U.S. They liked the way it **clung** to things in a garden. People dug holes and planted **kudzu**.

But there is a problem. **Kudzu** grows too well here! It likes the sun and warm days. **Kudzu** spreads quickly. Clumps of it grow up power poles and anything else the **vines** touch. The **vines** grow on trees. The trees die because they cannot get enough sun.

You can tug on **kudzu** or spray it with weed killer but it won't come off. It is hard to get rid of, and it is here to stay.

©Voyager Expanded Learning, L.P.

LESSON 4

 FLUENCY With a partner, read the paragraphs from the previous day's text. Follow along as your partner reads and check each other for reading errors.

A

1.	thick	that	thin	this
2.	fern	pitcher	her	clerk
3.	thud	them	jerk	stern
4.	trap	plant	stuck	lands

B

1.	answer	another	there	together
2.	other	friend	because	brought
3.	touch	snaps	bug	enough

C

1. _____	**4.** _____
2. _____	**5.** _____
3. _____	**6.** _____

VOCABULARY

1. carnivorous _____

_____

2. digest _____

_____

3. stalk _____

_____

4. pitcher _____

_____

Meat Eaters

How would you answer the question, "What is a plant?" You would probably say that a plant is a living thing that makes its own food. You probably would not say that a plant is a meat eater, would you?

Some plants are indeed meat eaters! We call them **carnivorous** *plants. The word* **carnivorous** *means "eating mainly animals." While* **carnivorous** *plants don't eat hamburgers or steaks, they do eat bugs. A* **carnivorous** *plant attracts an insect. It then captures it and absorbs it. The plant gets its nutrients from the insect it* **digests***.*

So, should you fear these meat-eating plants? The answer is no. The special chemicals they use to **digest** *insects are weak. They cannot hurt people.*

Three Meat Eaters

There are hundreds of meat-eating plants. One is the Venus flytrap. It has trigger hairs at the end of its leaves. They let the plant know when a bug is on the leaf. The thick leaves snap shut. The bug is stuck. The Venus flytrap **digests** the bug.

Another meat eater is a sundew. It has bright **stalks** on its leaves. When a bug lands on the **stalks**, it gets stuck there. The sundew **digests** the bug.

A third meat eater is the pitcher plant. It is shaped like a **pitcher**. When a bug falls into the **pitcher**, it gets stuck there. The pitcher plant **digests** the bug.

A

1.	dab	steps	ones	stop
2.	sick	these	smelled	buds
3.	people	plants	thick	kids
4.	others	helping	then	bug

B

1. _____ 4. _____
2. _____ 5. _____
3. _____ 6. _____

FLUENCY

C

1. There are a lot of plants . . . (paragraph 1)
2. Dogs and other pets . . . (paragraph 2)
3. . . . the plant can make you sick . . . (paragraph 3)

Killer Plants

Some people do not like carnivorous plants or kudzu. But these plants are not the ones to fear. There are a lot of plants that can make you ill. Some can even kill you.

Young kids get sick from plants. They smell the plants. Then they snip buds, nuts, and stalks. They put them to their lips and digest these parts. Dogs and other pets are attracted to the same plants. They get sick this way, too.

Some plants are used for medicine. But if you digest too much, the plant can make you sick or kill you.

The best way to stay safe from these plants is to get to know them. Learn the facts about your house plants. Help others. Tell them about plants that can make you sick.

PRACTICE AND APPLY

Complete the paragraph.

Some people fear meat-eating _____ plants. Others worry

about fast-growing _____. However, people should worry more

about some plants that might grow in and around their homes. Some parts of these

plants are pretty so kids and pets are _____ to them. Other

parts, like the stalks, are used as _____ to help you feel better.

But if you _____ too much of these plants you may become ill.

FLUENCY With a partner, take turns reading the paragraphs from the Lesson 5 Independent Reading passage. Follow along as your partner reads and check each other for reading errors.

A

1.	turn	dirt	surf	birth
2.	third	hurt	burn	stir
3.	stern	curl	that	fern
4.	camping	lung	term	frogs

B

1.	world	air	below	into
2.	another	together	people	there
3.	stress	answer	must	stomp

C

1.	_____	4.	_____
2.	_____	5.	_____
3.	_____	6.	_____

VOCABULARY

Naming Words	Action Words
_____	_____
_____	_____
_____	_____
_____	_____

Swim-Hockey Anyone?

What is your favorite sport? Perhaps you like to swim or play hockey. Underwater hockey **combines** *both hockey and swimming.*

Any person can play underwater hockey. You can be a girl or boy. You can be large or small. You do need to be able to swim. You also need to wear fins, a mask, and a **snorkel***. Wear a glove and headgear to keep from getting hurt.*

The game is played on the bottom of a swimming pool. There are two teams. Each has six players. The game begins in the middle of the pool. Players pass a heavy puck by **hurling** *it with a stick. Players score by hitting the puck into the underwater net.*

Odd Sports

There are different sports around the world. The caber toss is a sport in Scotland. A caber looks like a power pole. A player picks up the caber and **hurls** it. The caber flips in the air then lands in the dirt.

In Asia, people play a game called sepak takraw. This game **combines** volleyball and soccer. The goal is to score the most points. Like volleyball, the serving team scores a point when the other team cannot get the ball back over the net. The trick is, players cannot use their hands. They must kick the ball over the net!

A third odd sport is waterfall kayaking. The kayakers **surge** down a waterfall into the surf below. These people have nerves of steel!

FLUENCY With a partner, take turns reading the paragraphs from the Lesson 6 Independent Reading passage. Follow along as your partner reads and check each other for reading errors.

A

1.	b<u>oi</u>l	t<u>oi</u>l	sp<u>oi</u>l	m<u>oi</u>st
2.	<u>sh</u>irt	ru<u>sh</u>	fla<u>sh</u>	<u>sh</u>ed
3.	join	point	mush	cash
4.	trap	plant	stuck	lands

B

1.	nights	only	great	again
2.	world	answer	below	air
3.	term	into	burn	bird

C

1. _____		**4.** _____
2. _____		**5.** _____
3. _____		**6.** _____

VOCABULARY

1. To be fit and ready to do something is to ☐☐☐☐☐☐☐ .

2. To work hard for a long time is to ☐☐☐☐ .

3. A person who drives a dogsled team is a ☐☐☐☐☐☐ .

4. The winner of a contest can claim ☐☐☐☐☐☐☐ .

A Musher's Journal

February 20, 2005

*To enter and finish the Iditarod has been a life-long dream of mine. Now my wish has come true. After **toiling** to complete two 400-mile races, I have **qualified** to enter the "Last Great Race on Earth."*

I began training back in July. I took the dogs on short runs of five miles. By the first snowfall in October, the dogs were *ready for longer runs. By December, we were mushing 50 miles a day.*

*The dogs and I will arrive in Anchorage, Alaska, next week. I am prepared for the race. My goal is not to finish first or even win a prize. My goal is to simply cross the finish line with my dogs. That will be a **victory** for me.*

A Musher's Journal

March 15, 2005

What a rush! I was the 50th **musher** to cross the finish line. Hundreds of people were there. They pointed, waved, and clapped. There were flashes of light as people took pictures. It was such a wonderful feeling. I joined the small group of **mushers** to finish the Iditarod.

The race was more difficult than I'd thought it would be. The cold, blinding snow was something I'll never forget. The nights seemed to last forever. Getting to each checkpoint was a **victory**. It was the only way I knew I was going the right way.

I'm thinking of entering again next year. It truly is a great race!

FLUENCY With a partner, take turns reading the Lesson 7 Independent Reading journal entry. Imagine you are the author when it is your turn to read. When it is your partner's turn, read along and check for reading errors.

A

1.	h<u>ar</u>sh	f<u>ar</u>	h<u>ar</u>d	b<u>ar</u>k
2.	<u>wh</u>en	<u>wh</u>iz	<u>wh</u>ack	<u>wh</u>iff
3.	part	wharf	start	whip
4.	stern	soil	shirt	crash

B

1.	push	climb	heavy	pull
2.	great	there	night	again
3.	smirk	answer	only	broil

C

1.	_____	4.	_____
2.	_____	5.	_____
3.	_____	6.	_____

VOCABULARY

Remember When . . .

Have you ever played tug-of-war? Did you know it was once an Olympic sport? There are many events that were once in the **Olympic Games**.

In 1900, underwater swimming was an Olympic **event**. *The race was 60-meters, or about 200 feet. Swimmers earned two points for each meter they swam and one point for each second they stayed underwater.*

Golf was an Olympic **event** *in 1900 and 1904. In 1908, people at the Olympics took part in motor boating. And for several years, people had* **competitions** *to see who could be the fastest to dart up a rope. In 1932, an American was the last to win the rope-climbing event when he climbed just over 26 feet in less than seven seconds.*

Inuit Games

Some people in Alaska are called Inuit, or Eskimos. They have **competitions** like the **Olympic Games**. Long ago, the **events** were made to test hunters. Today the Inuit still compete in these **events**.

The head pull is like tug-of-war. But you try to pull the headband off your partner! There is also an ear weight **contest** in which you hang heavy weights from your ear. Then you see how far you can walk. To start the **knuckle** hop, you get into a push up position. However, you get on your **knuckles** instead of the palm of your hand. Then you push off the floor and hop as far as you can. It is hard!

LESSON 9

With a partner, take turns reading sentences from the Lesson 8 Independent Reading passage. One partner reads one sentence while the other partner reads along and checks for errors. Then the other partner reads one sentence. Complete the passage.

A

1.	r<u>oa</u>d	g<u>oa</u>l	b<u>oa</u>st	t<u>oa</u>st
2.	<u>qu</u>ack	<u>qu</u>est	<u>qu</u>ick	<u>qu</u>iz
3.	quilt	loan	coat	groan
4.	whisk	star	smart	crush

B

1.	their	eyes	yours	move
2.	climb	pull	heavy	great
3.	push	sunk	spark	whiff

C

1. _____	4.	_____
2. _____	5.	_____
3. _____	6.	_____

VOCABULARY

1. interview _____
_____

2. streak _____
_____

3. dugout _____
_____

4. superstition_____
_____

Sports Superstitions

Justin followed Mark onto the football field. "Just one more question. Why did you just do that?"

"What?" asked Mark in an annoyed voice.

"You just ate grass from the end zone!"

*"It's good luck. I'll score one touchdown or field goal for each piece of grass I eat. The **interview** is over, Justin."*

*Justin walked away, adding Mark's **superstition** to a list.*

Justin's list:
- *For good luck, wipe the soles of your shoes before playing basketball.*
- *In baseball, spit into your hand before going to bat.*
- *When fishing, spit on your bait before casting.*
- *Carry coins in your pocket during golf.*
- *For each piece of grass eaten, score one touchdown or one field goal.*

*Justin decided that doing these silly **superstitions** couldn't hurt!*

Good Luck, Amber

All eyes were on Coach Joan. "This is the end of the road," she said. "This is the end of our quest for the state softball championship. Let's play like we've played all season. Go Red Coats!"

The girls went to their places to start the game. "Liz," said Amber, "you're on a roll! Pitch another no-hitter!"

"Amber!" shouted Liz. "Don't you know it's bad luck to boast about a pitcher's **streak**?"

Amber moaned and walked into the **dugout**. When she saw Meg, she said, "I don't have my bat. Can you loan me yours?"

"Amber," groaned Meg, "Don't you know it's bad luck to use someone else's bat?"

Angrily, Amber spit into her hand, grabbed a team bat, and left the dugout. "Now that," laughed Meg, "is good luck!"

A

1. road	when	quick	start
2. push	heavy	dirt	goal
3. quest	jerk	dash	hurt
4. again	firm	pull	crash

B

1. _____   4. _____
2. _____   5. _____
3. _____   6. _____

C

1. . . . joining a sport called cyclocross. (paragraph 1)

2. . . . the event is on firm dirt. (paragraph 2)

3. . . . getting hurt if they crash. (paragraph 4)

INDEPENDENT READING

Riding Cyclocross

Many people are joining a sport called cyclocross. Its name gives a hint about it. Cyclocross is a bike race. But it is not on a road.

It is a competition. It combines riding and running. Part of the event is on firm dirt. Riders can go fast or coast. But the event also has mud, water, and cliffs. Riders must be quick to get off their bikes when something is in their way. They jerk up on the heavy bike and carry it. Then they dash through the mud or over the thing in their way. Streaks of mud line the path.

When the path is clear, the bikers start riding again. They may not get far before they must get off again.

Teams toil to have a victory. Riders wear gear to keep them from getting hurt if they crash.

PRACTICE AND APPLY

Write the vocabulary words in alphabetical order on the lines below. Then draw lines to match vocabulary words with examples.

1. _____   Pull weeds in a garden

2. _____   A race with teams of dogs and their mushers

3. _____   Lines of red paint on the sides of a car

4. _____   Puts oil and an egg in the cake mix

5. _____   A prize in a singing contest

6. _____   Ice-skating at the Winter Olympics

FLUENCY With four other students, read the Lesson 9 Independent Reading passage as a play. Read the parts for the narrator, Coach Joan, Amber, Liz, and Meg. Then read the passage again, playing the part of a different person.

A

1.	leap	treat	clean	steal
2.	look	soon	tool	good
3.	speak	proof	meal	hoop
4.	soap	quit	card	soil

B

1.	thought	idea	follow	new
2.	yours	heavy	world	move
3.	their	sharp	float	air

C

1. _____   4. _____

2. _____   5. _____

3. _____   6. _____

VOCABULARY

1. _____ Hula Hoop

2. _____ FBI man

3. _____ car insurance saleswoman

4. _____ Pogo Stick

5. _____ Band-Aids

6. _____ Bubble Gum

7. _____ IRS (tax) person

8. _____ Yo-Yo

9. _____ real estate salesman

10. _____ 007 in the Secret Service

Bonus:

11. _____   12. _____

Be an Inventor

People have been inventing things for thousands of years. They invented tools for hunting. They learned to use fire to heat their food and light their homes.

*Today, people are still inventing. Some modern **inventions** are completely new. Others improve on older **inventions**. Most **inventions** begin with a problem.*

You can be an inventor, too. First, make a list of everyday problems. For example, I always forget where I leave my boots. I cannot neatly make my bed.

Next, choose a problem that you think is interesting and can be solved.

*List ways to solve the problem. Review your list and choose a **solution** you think will work. Draw a picture of how your **invention** will work. The next step is to build a model of your **invention**. This often takes the help of an adult.*

*You may need to **tweak** your plan. But stick to it! You may become a famous inventor.*

Keep Your Invention Safe

You followed the **invention** steps. Look! You have an **invention**! You want to sell it to stores soon. But, someone could steal your idea.

The **government** has a tool to keep that from happening. It is a **patent**. A **patent** is a piece of paper. It says that only the person who thought of the **invention** can make it and sell it.

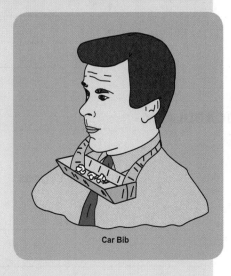

Car Bib

Getting a **patent** is not easy. The **invention** must be useful. It must also be something new. You need proof that you are the first person to invent the item. You must be the first person to speak of it or show it to another person.

It costs a lot of money to get a **patent**. Speak with a good **patent agent**. A **patent agent** can lead you in the right direction. He or she can help you decide whether or not to get a **patent**.

With a partner, take turns reading each paragraph from the Lesson 11 Independent Reading passage. Follow along as your partner reads and check each other for reading errors.

A

1.	m<u>e</u>	g<u>o</u>	m<u>y</u>	sh<u>e</u>
2.	f<u>or</u>	f<u>or</u>t	sh<u>or</u>t	c<u>or</u>n
3.	snort	why	so	be
4.	quill	broom	foam	heat

B

1.	Earth	sure	choose	doctor
2.	follow	new	climb	thought
3.	eyes	beam	idea	smooth

C

1.	_____	4.	_____
2.	_____	5.	_____
3.	_____	6.	_____

VOCABULARY

Naming Words	**Action Words**
_____	_____
_____	_____
_____	_____
_____	_____
_____	_____

Under Siege

Brian stared at the picture in the magazine. It showed a drawing of an 800-year-old castle under attack. Brian could imagine the castle's lord and lady safely inside while the knights and soldiers kept the castle safe during the **siege**. *He knew that one* **siege** *could last for months.*

Brian's eyes scanned the picture. He studied the old weapons that he found so interesting. Several men had to **operate** *the large trebuchet. It slung huge boulders or burning material over the castle walls. Similarly, the ballista fired stones or spears at enemies. Next, Brian studied the battering ram. Enemies used the huge tree trunks to ram the castle. They would try to smash into castle walls.*

Brian looked at the picture. He wanted to go to Europe and see a real castle. But for now, he would learn by reading about strong forts.

The Most Important Invention

My class has a task. We are to write a report about an invention. We are to choose the most important invention of the 20th **century**. I cannot decide. So many are important.

Take a look into the sky. Air travel has changed the way we travel from place to place. Planes fly. Space shuttles **orbit** Earth and return to be used again.

Turn on a computer. You can send a short message to a friend. You can order **products**. You can track a storm or check the weather.

You sniff and snort. You cry. You can visit a doctor for help. He or she can give you a **prescription** for medicine. You soon feel better.

I cannot write about one invention. So, my report will be about all of these. I'll make sure I tell why each is "the most important."

FLUENCY With a partner, take turns reading the complete Independent Reading passage from Lesson 12. Follow along as your partner reads and check each other for reading errors.

A

1.	free	need	beep	feel
2.	hopped	patting	hugged	napping
3.	stopped	nagging	seem	keep
4.	dry	shook	horn	pool

B

1.	mild	young	imagine	guess
2.	idea	doctor	Earth	new
3.	neat	sure	choose	sky

C

1. _____   4. _____
2. _____   5. _____
3. _____   6. _____

VOCABULARY

Things run by electricity	Things automatic and electric
_____	_____
_____	_____
_____	_____
_____	_____

Useless Inventions

Most inventors hope their inventions make life better for people. Unfortunately, some inventions seem useless!

One inventor liked to skate. But he did not like taking his skates off before he went shopping or to a restaurant. So he invented knee skates. You wear them on your knee and shin. You have to kneel down to skate, but you get to keep your shoes on your feet. When you finish skating, you don't have to stop and change back into your shoes.

*Many people mow their lawns. One inventor tried to improve the lawnmower. He **attached** a lawnmower blade to a tricycle. If you don't mind looking and feeling a little odd, you can pedal your way to a nice-looking lawn! Or, maybe cutting the lawn could become a two-year old's job? That idea would probably be snipped by a parent!*

Inventions for Lazy Pet Owners and Parents

Everyone agrees that little kids and pets need to be hugged and petted. But sometimes you want your hands free. At those times, you need the **automatic** pet petter. When your dog or young child is nagging or yapping for you to pet or hold it, send it to the pet petter. The machine has a scanning **electric** eye. When it senses a pet or child, it swings its human-like hand. The rubbing and patting will keep the little one feeling happy. Just look at that wagging tail or grinning face!

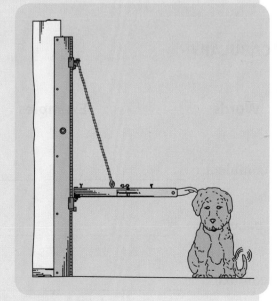

Imagine that a baby is napping or sitting happily on the floor. You wonder if her diaper is wet or dry. But you don't want to peek. You need the diaper alarm! Put the **sensor** on the diaper. When the diaper becomes wet, a mild **current** of **electricity** passes to the **sensor**. Lights flash and an alarm beeps. No more guessing!

With a partner, take turns reading paragraphs from the Lesson 13 Independent Reading passage. Read the paragraphs as if they were from a news report. Follow along as your partner reads and check each other for reading errors.

A

1.	f<u>ir</u>st	sp<u>ur</u>	p<u>er</u>k	b<u>ur</u>n
2.	c<u>ar</u>t	st<u>or</u>k	h<u>ar</u>m	sh<u>or</u>t
3.	start	firm	forks	doom
4.	stream	shook	fry	pump

B

1.	science	school	learn	loves
2.	young	wheel	thought	mild
3.	guess	sure	imagine	sweep

C

1.	_____	4.	_____
2.	_____	5.	_____
3.	_____	6.	_____

VOCABULARY

Words	Examples	Non-examples
confident	_____	_____
patients	_____	_____
confidant	_____	_____
patience	_____	_____

Martina's Robot Team

Martina walked into the Georgia Dome. She couldn't believe how huge the place was. Martina and her teammates were there with people from 20 other countries, including Denmark, Germany, Norway, South Korea, and Turkey. They were there to compete in the FIRST LEGO® League competition. FIRST stands for For Inspiration and Recognition of Science and **Technology**. *It's for kids aged 9 to 14.*

Martina's team took their places. They were ready to start the robot-building competition. The robots they build are made of LEGOS® with sensors, motors, and gears. The robots must be able to perform nine different tasks. The robot arms must turn, open a gate, and climb stairs.

Martina felt **confident** *about her team. They had practiced. They were here to build the best robot and to have fun.*

Dean Kamen: Inventor

Dean Kamen enjoys inventing and turning students to science. Kamen brought these two loves together when he started FIRST (For Inspiration and Recognition of Science and **Technology**). It **spurs** middle and high school students to learn more about science.

Kamen has a long history of inventing and solving problems. He has more than 150 patents. When Kamen's brother was learning to be a doctor, he told Kamen that it was hard to give some **patients** medicine. Kamen took charge. He invented an automatic pump. It gives **patients** their medicine easily.

Kamen invented the Segway®. It is a two-wheeled "Human **Transporter**." It is easy to operate a Segway®. You step on, hold on with your arms, and lean in the direction you want to go. The Segway® does the rest. Kamen thought about the human body when he invented the Segway®. We can stand upright. When we are off **balance**, we take a step forward. The sensors, control system, and motor work in a similar way.

A

1.	wheel	hurt	he	idea
2.	loves	science	locker	took
3.	dirt	school	hopped	feet
4.	hard	young	sure	born

B

1.	_____	**4.**	_____
2.	_____	**5.**	_____
3.	_____	**6.**	_____

FLUENCY

C

1. . . . do you know about the young inventors . . . (paragraph 1)

2. . . . students' backpacks were hurting their backs . . . (paragraph 2)

3. . . . skateboard could not take the shock . . . (paragraph 3)

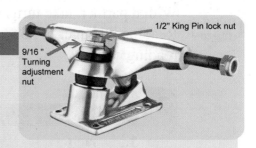

9/16 "
Turning
adjustment
nut

1/2" King Pin lock nut

INDEPENDENT READING

Young Inventors Solve Problems

You may know about Alexander Graham Bell's telephone and the Wright brothers' airplane. But do you know about the young inventors Rikio and Ole?

Rikio's sister's back hurt. She carried a heavy backpack. Other students' backpacks were hurting their backs, too. You could get backpacks with wheels. But they would not fit in the school lockers. Rikio had a solution. He invented wheels that you can attach to a backpack. You can pull it behind you. Then, when you need to put the backpack in your locker, you take them off.

One day Ole was on his skateboard. He hopped and took a jump. He landed hard and broke his foot. There was a problem. The skateboard could not take the shock of a hard landing. Ole had an idea. His father helped him build the "O-shock" to ease the shock of a hard landing. Ole has a patent for his invention. The O-shock is now sold in stores.

PRACTICE AND APPLY

Complete the crossword puzzle using the passage from this lesson.

Across

1. Ole landed so _____ he broke his foot.

5. Carrying a heavy backpack can make one's back _____.

6. Ole got a _____ from the government to protect his invention.

8. Rikio and Ole are young _____ with new ideas.

Down

2. Rikio found a new way to _____ wheels to backpacks.

3. The _____ on the bottom of old backpacks made them too big for a school locker.

4. Ole's _____ was a new kind of skateboard.

7. Ole _____ his skateboard over a curb.

FLUENCY

With a partner, take turns reading each paragraph from the Lesson 14 Independent Reading passage. Follow along as your partner reads and check each other for reading errors.

A

1.	su<u>ch</u>	<u>ch</u>irp	spe<u>ech</u>	mun<u>ch</u>
2.	br<u>ai</u>n	f<u>ai</u>nt	n<u>ai</u>l	p<u>ai</u>n
3.	teacher	wait	main	chart
4.	seat	by	sport	sleep

B

1.	care	charge	watch	changes
2.	science	learn	only	climb
3.	burst	loves	idea	slipped

C

1. _____		**4.** _____
2. _____		**5.** _____
3. _____		**6.** _____

VOCABULARY

Illness: _____

Symptoms	**Prevention**
_____	_____
_____	_____
_____	_____
_____	_____

Your Amazing Brain

Put your fists together. Your brain is about that size. It weighs about three pounds, or about as much as your science book.

*Your brain has different parts. The main part is on top. It is the **cerebrum**. It looks like a wrinkled lump of jelly. A lot of activity takes place here. When you munch your favorite food, the **cerebrum** is the part of the brain that recognizes the taste. It helps you feel pain. It receives messages from your eyes, ears, and other body parts.*

Messages come into the brain and go to different places. There are areas for speech, hearing, and other senses.

*Your teacher tells you to write your name on a chart. Or, you go ride a skateboard. You do these things almost without thinking. That is thanks to a part of the brain called the **cerebellum**. It sends messages to the body's muscles.*

The brain stem connects the brain to the spinal cord. The brain stem controls your breathing, heartbeat, and digestion.

Protect Your Brain

Your brain is important. You are in charge of taking care of it.

A fall or bump on the head can cause a brain **injury**. The best way to **protect** your brain is to **prevent** an **injury** from happening.

Do these things to **prevent** a brain **injury**:

- Wear a seat belt in a car.
- Wear a helmet when you: ride a bike, motorcycle, or ATV; play a sport such as football or baseball; use in-line skates or ride a skateboard; ski or snowboard.
- Avoid falls in your home by: picking up things you might trip on, such as toys. Put a mat in the bathtub.

If you faint, fall, or bump your head, watch for these **symptoms**. They can signal a brain **injury**. If you have these **symptoms**, call a doctor right away. **Symptoms**: head or neck pain; trouble remembering things or thinking; slowed speech; changes in sleep; trouble seeing, smelling, tasting, or hearing.

With a partner, take turns reading paragraphs from the Lesson 16 Independent Reading passage. The first partner reads the first three paragraphs. The second partner reads the rest of the passage. Follow along as your partner reads and check each other for reading errors.

A

1.	bone	home	drove	white
2.	nine	slide	game	brave
3.	cast	reach	turn	weeks
4.	arm	third	weak	wait

B

1.	tonight	colors	diary	muscle
2.	charge	thought	watch	care
3.	young	healed	third	changes

C

1. _____	**4.** _____
2. _____	**5.** _____
3. _____	**6.** _____

VOCABULARY

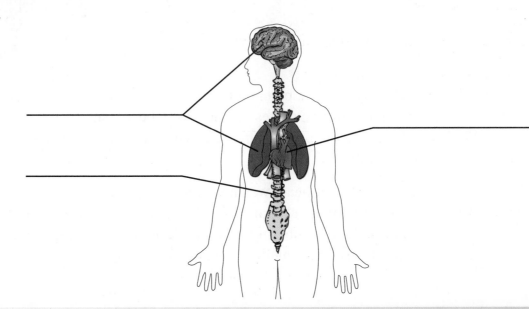

Your Bones

"The hip bone's connected to the leg bone . . ." You may know that song. Bones are worth singing about. Without them, we would be like a jellyfish—a blob. Bones help hold you up. They are your body's frame. Your frame is made up of 206 bones.

*The 32 bones in your arms and fingers allow you to reach out and grab things. Similarly, the 31 bones in your legs and feet allow you to walk and run. The 26 bones in your **spine** help you bend over and stand up straight.*

*Bones have other jobs, too. They protect your softer **organs**. The hard skull protects the brain. Think of your ribs as a cage made of bones. Inside the cage are your **heart** and lungs.*

*Bones are hard on the outside and soft on the inside. The inside is made of **marrow**. The jelly-like **marrow** makes red and white blood **cells**. A **cell** is the basic unit of every living thing.*

Protect your bones. They are hard and they are able to bend slightly. Yet, they can break. Take steps to prevent broken bones.

Jake's Diary

June 5: We had a baseball game tonight. We were winning nine to five. It was my turn at bat. The pitch was perfect. I hit the ball. I made it to third base. I could see the second baseman throwing the ball to home base. I decided to slide to make a home run. As I slid into home base, I fell on my arm. I yelled in pain. Although I scored a run, I was afraid I broke the bone.

Dad drove me to the hospital. I was brave as they x-rayed the bone. I broke a bone all right! The doctor put on a red cast. Yea! Red and white are my team's colors.

July 11: It's been five weeks since I broke my arm and I just got my cast off. I thought it would hurt, but it didn't. I can finally move my arm, but it is weak. I'm going to have to work to make the muscle stronger. At least the bone is healed back in one piece!

With a partner, take turns reading journal entries from the Lesson 17 Independent Reading passage. The first partner reads the first entry. The second partner reads the second entry. Follow along as your partner reads and check each other for reading errors.

A

1. day	clay	spray	tray
2. couch	out	south	shout
3. stay	pouch	mouth	way
4. name	side	waste	lunch

B

1. stomach	students	through	does
2. muscle	tonight	science	choose
3. wide	plain	diary	colors

C

1. _____	**4.** _____
2. _____	**5.** _____
3. _____	**6.** _____

VOCABULARY

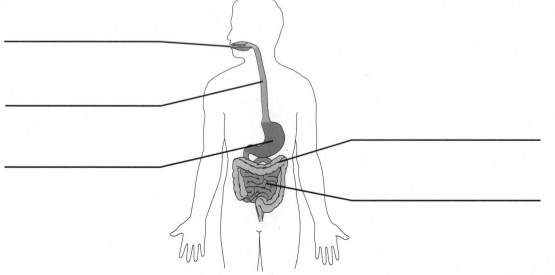

A Lesson in Digestion

Ray's class was learning about the **digestive system**. *"Which is stronger, our bones or our teeth?" asked Mr. Couch.*

"Bones!" the class yelled.

Mr. Couch chuckled. "The answer is your teeth! They are stronger than most rocks."

Mr. Couch asked the class if they know what happens to food after the teeth finish chewing it. "It's really an amazing process!" said Mr. Couch.

"Picture a battery–operated piggy bank inside our bodies. Instead of coins, we take in food," explained Mr. Couch with a smile. "The tongue pushes food to the back of the mouth. Muscles in the throat push the food down into the **esophagus**. *The* **esophagus** *then pushes the food into the stomach."*

"The stomach," Mr. Couch continued, "is like a pouch lined with strong muscles. The pouch expands as you eat and drink. Acid is released from the stomach wall. It breaks down the food. Then the stomach's muscles squeeze the food and acid together. After a few hours, it is a thick mush. It leaves your stomach and continues its digestive journey."

Just then, Ray's stomach growled loudly. "It must be time for lunch," he said.

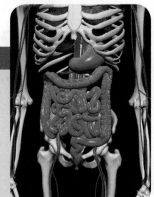

A Second Lesson in Digestion

After lunch, Mr. Couch went on with his talk on the **digestive system**. "Your food becomes a thick mush in your stomach. Then it moves into your small **intestine**. But don't let its name fool you."

Mr. Couch had Ray and two other students come to the front of the room. They raised their arms out to the side. They stood with their fingertips touching.

"This is about how long your small **intestine** is," Mr. Couch explained. "It is about an inch wide. **Nutrients** pass through the small **intestine** and into your body."

"What's left of your food makes its way around your small **intestine**. Then, it goes into your large **intestine**. Your large **intestine** is much shorter than the small **intestine**. It's only about five feet long. But it is wider."

Ray asked, "Does it matter whether we eat junk food or healthy food since it all turns to mush?"

Mr. Couch answered, "Would you rather have a piggy bank full of pennies or silver dollars?"

The whole class laughed and yelled, "Silver dollars!"

With two other students, read the Lesson 18 Independent Reading passage as a play. After the first reading, choose another part and read the passage again. Follow along as others read and check each other for reading errors.

A

1.	s<u>igh</u>t	h<u>igh</u>	fr<u>igh</u>t	m<u>igh</u>t
2.	sigh	bright	light	right
3.	sounds	slight	side	waves
4.	bones	loud	flight	sway

B

1.	ears	travel	canal	vacuum
2.	through	colors	stomach	does
3.	students	watch	screech	gray

C

1. _____   **4.** _____

2. _____   **5.** _____

3. _____   **6.** _____

VOCABULARY

A	B	C	D	E	F	G	H	I	J	K	L	M	N	O	P	Q	R	S	T	U	V	W	X	Y	Z
3	5	9	✓	✖	✳	▲	❙	✛	☙	◯	◗	■	✿	☉	❖	◆	✤	★	✦	●	◉	✛	⊛	✳	✲

1. ✳ ● ✿ ✿ ✖ ◗   _____

_____

2. ❖ ✛ ✦ 9 ❙   _____

_____

3. ✿ ✖ ✤ ◉ ✖ ★   _____

_____

4. ☉ ✛ 5 ✤ 3 ✦ ✖   _____

_____

Your Sense of Sight

We find out about the world around us by using our senses. The five senses are sight, hearing, smell, taste, and touch.

Your eyes see colors and detect the brightness of light. The eyes take in the information and **transform** *it into* **signals***. These* **signals** *travel along* **nerves** *to your brain. Your brain makes sense of the* **signals** *and tells you what you see.*

If you look at your eye, you will see a colored part. This is your iris. It might be brown, green, or blue. In the center of your iris is a dark spot. This is your pupil. The pupil changes size. You can watch this happen. Take a hand-held mirror into a room with low light. Look at your pupils. They will be large. They are open wide to let in lots of light. Turn on the light. Your pupils will quickly get smaller. This happens so that too much light doesn't enter the eye.

Your Sense of Hearing

Your ear is more than the bendable skin on the side of your head. It helps you learn about the world around you by hearing sound.

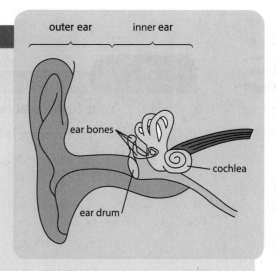

All sounds travel in waves. Your outer ear acts like a **funnel**. It sends the sound waves into a tunnel. This is called the ear canal. The sound waves **vibrate** your eardrum at the end of the ear canal. They go past the three smallest bones in your body. The sound waves turn into **signals**. The ear sends these to the brain through **nerves**. Your brain tells you what it is that you hear.

You hear different kinds of sounds. Some have a high **pitch**. Others have a low **pitch**. We measure how loud something is in decibels. A whisper is about 20 decibels. A vacuum cleaner is about 75 decibels. A jet airplane in flight is about 130 decibels. If you listen to sounds louder than 90 decibels for a long time, you might harm your ears.

A

1. clench	travel	frail	scout
2. watch	whole	side	stay
3. flight	muscle	chart	brain
4. day	changes	through	sight

B

1. _____   4. _____

2. _____   5. _____

3. _____   6. _____

FLUENCY

C

1. Your heart is about as big . . . (paragraph 1)

2. . . . blood travels through your whole body. (paragraph 3)

3. . . . heartbeat does not stay the same. (paragraph 4)

INDEPENDENT READING

Your Amazing Heart

You may remember that your brain is about the same size as two fists put together. Take away one fist. Your heart is about as big as one fist.

Your heart is one of your body's organs. It is also a muscle. It works day and night all your life.

You have probably felt your heartbeat. Do you know what it is? You can think of your heart as two bags side by side in your chest. The left bag fills up with blood. Then the heart muscle squeezes. It pushes the blood out of the heart. The blood travels through your whole body. When the heart relaxes, it fills up with blood again. The heart's squeezing and releasing is your heartbeat. It's like clenching and relaxing your fist.

Your heartbeat does not stay the same. It raises and lowers. When you bike or skate, your muscles need more blood. Your heart beats faster, speeding up the flow of blood. When you sleep, your muscles do not need as much blood. Your heartbeat slows. Chart your heartbeat before and after you run.

PRACTICE AND APPLY

Draw a picture of a body part you read about in Lessons 16–20. Then write a description of it. Look back in the passages for ideas.

With a partner, take turns reading the Lesson 19 Independent Reading passage. The first partner reads the complete passage. Then the second partner reads the complete passage. Follow along as your partner reads and check each other for reading errors.

A

1.	knit	knight	knife	knack
2.	hall	malt	stall	salt
3.	scald	wall	kneel	knock
4.	pays	screen	round	starred

B

1.	favorite	money	earn	believe
2.	vacuum	travel	loud	watch
3.	paints	canal	ears	clinch

C

1. _____	**4.** _____
2. _____	**5.** _____
3. _____	**6.** _____

VOCABULARY

Mom had a long day at work. Before she came home, I cleaned the kitchen. I wanted to surprise her. When she came home, she was thrilled. She said we both _____ a treat. A friend at work had given Mom two movie tickets. So, we went to the movie _____. We saw an _____. We were both _____.

Seeing a Movie

I buy my ticket outside. Then I stand in line for popcorn with salt and a soda. I walk down the long, dark hall to **theater** *number 2. It's showing the movie I've been waiting to see. I always enjoy seeing my favorite actor. I know I'm going to like the film because certain people are in it.*

I walk in and choose the perfect seat. As I sit down, I hope that the people around me will not talk to each other or make calls on their cell phones.

The lights slowly dim. I look up at the movie screen. It's as big as the entire wall. I'm ready to be **entertained**.

What kind of movie do you like to watch? Some people enjoy movies so scary that their knuckles turn white from gripping the edges of their seats. Others like movies with knights and queens. Personally, I like movies that make me laugh.

Highly Paid Actors

Do you have a favorite movie actor? Can you name all the films he or she has starred in? Do you know how much money your favorite actor earns for doing just one film?

Several actresses earn an **income** of at least $12 million for one movie. These actresses include Jennifer Lopez, Angelina Jolie, Halle Berry, and Reese Witherspoon. Cameron Diaz and Julia Roberts make about $20 million for one film. Diaz earned about $10 million for *Shrek 2*. For this movie, she only had to talk. She was the voice of the princess in the **animated film**.

Men are also high earners. In fact, they often make more than actresses. Will Smith and Johnny Depp earn about $20 million for each film they star in. Tom Cruise, Jim Carrey, Mike Myers, and Adam Sandler earn about $25 million for each film. Like Diaz, Myers earned about $10 million for talking in *Shrek 2*.

You may wonder if these people **deserve** the high pay. Some people believe they do. Altogether, Tom Cruise's films have earned more than $2 billion. Just one of Cameron Diaz's films earned more than $100 million. Similarly, Jim Carrey's film *Bruce Almighty* earned almost $245 million. So, do you think the actors **deserve** the high pay? What's your call?

Follow along as your partner reads the first two paragraphs from the Lesson 21 Independent Reading passage. Then you read the final two paragraphs while your partner reads along. Check each other for reading errors.

A

1.	slid*ing*	tast*ing*	mak*ing*	div*ing*
2.	shap*ed*	lik*ed*	vot*ed*	chok*ed*
3.	raking	smiled	lined	fading
4.	pound	sighed	jars	pools

B

1.	pictures	giant	minutes	building
2.	outer	maze	favorite	believe
3.	earn	food	carved	money

C

1.	_____	4.	_____
2.	_____	5.	_____
3.	_____	6.	_____

VOCABULARY

_____

Festival

Fun Festivals

Festivals *are a form of entertainment. Most* **festivals** *have things in common, such as food and music. But some* **festivals** *are* **unique***.*

Has anyone ever told you not to play with your food? If you go to Buñol, Spain, no one will say that. They have a tomato fight **festival***. You'll see people biting into tomatoes and then throwing them. You'll be slipping and sliding in red tomato sauce. No one will be baking with those tomatoes!*

Do you like tasting baby food? Then the Baby Food **Festival** *is for you. Facing a blindfolded partner, you try to eat five jars of baby food your partner feeds to you. You'll be wiping baby food off of your face for days!*

Maybe you prefer something less messy. You can go to Canada for the Winterlude **Festival***. View huge blocks of ice that* **sculptors** *carved into animals, people, and buildings. Watch people skating through a frozen maze. There's even a movie on a giant screen made out of snow.*

No matter what you like, there is a **festival** *for you!*

Justin's Messy Festivals

Justin is nine. His family has an odd **habit**. They enjoy going to different **festivals**. You don't think that's odd? Well, they only go to messy **festivals**.

They just got back from Arizona's Mighty Mud Mania **festival**. "It was so much fun," said Justin. "We raced through the mud, sliding and diving into it."

Last year, Justin's family went to South Carolina's World **Grits Festival**. "I liked that **festival**!" Justin explained. "We lined up to be weighed. Then, one at a time, we jumped into a pool of **grits**. When I got out, I smiled and posed for a picture. Then I was weighed again. I didn't win. The person wearing the most **grits** wins. Dad placed second. For the rest of the day, everything tasted like **grits**."

Two years ago, Justin's family went to Coney Island, New York. They went to the Hot Dog Eating Contest. They almost choked when they saw the winner. He ate 50 hot dogs in just 12 minutes. "We faced the facts," said Justin. "We weren't going to win that contest. We didn't even want to try!"

With a partner, read the Lesson 22 Independent Reading passage as a news report. One partner reads what Justin says. The other partner reads the rest of the passage like a news anchor. Then switch roles and read the passage again. Follow along as your partner reads and check each other for reading errors.

A

1. graph	phonics	sulphur	dolphin
2. joy	oyster	ploy	employ
3. enjoy	toys	gopher	orphan
4. waving	knot	stall	baked

B

1. music	legal	create	argue
2. money	giant	picture	minutes
3. stalled	muscle	joking	building

C

1. _____	4. _____
2. _____	5. _____
3. _____	6. _____

VOCABULARY

communicate	download	emphasize
permission	phenomenon	upload

1. These two words are opposites. _____ and _____

2. Synonyms for this word are stress and highlight. _____

3. When you talk you do this. _____

4. When you ask a parent to let you spend the night away from home, you are asking for this. _____

5. One possible example of this is that everyone you know wants an iPod. _____

Computer Use on the Rise

Computers have become a form of entertainment and a way of life. People send e-mails to **communicate** *with others. They* **download** *everything from music to photos to ring tones for their cell phones. People use the Internet to buy products, pay bills, do research, and play games with people around the world. There are people who use a computer at work and at school. Many people have computers in their homes.*

Children and teenagers make up a large portion of computer users. They have access to computers at school, at public libraries, and in homes. According to one survey, close to 95 percent of all children ages 9 to 17 are computer users.

Computer use is on the rise. Just 20 years ago, the phrase "World Wide Web" was unknown to most people. Now the phrase has become part of our language. There were people who thought computers were a phase or that they were toys that would lose popularity. Those people were wrong. People today depend on their computers in many ways.

Downloading Music

Downloading music from Web sites is a **phenomenon**. Some of these Web sites are legal. The people who create the music have given **permission** for these sites to sell their songs. At these sites, you pay a small amount of money to **download** a song.

There are other sites that are not legal. This illegal process is called peer-to-peer (P2P) sharing. Someone **uploads** a song without getting **permission** from the music's creator. Then, other people go to the Web site and **download** the song for free. This is like stealing.

So, what if you enjoy music? Can you still **download** MP3 files? Yes, you just have to employ good judgment. You have to know which sites to use. Many artists have their own Web sites. If you want to hear music from a certain artist, search the Internet for his or her Web site. Many artists offer free downloads for their listeners to enjoy. You can also pay a fee and **download** from a legal Web site. There are many of these sites on the web.

Let me **emphasize** one point. Make sure you read each phrase in each paragraph on the Web site. You want to buy the music legally.

LESSON 24

With a small group of students, each takes a turn reading a sentence from the Lesson 23 Independent Reading passage. Continue until you have read the whole passage. Then read the passage a second time.

A

1.	study	dry	penny	fry
2.	studied	dried	pennies	fries
3.	tries	buddies	slight	hurried
4.	knock	enjoy	traded	dining

B

1.	excited	woman	important	forward
2.	music	legal	favorite	create
3.	knot	students	argue	knead

C

1.	_____	4.	_____
2.	_____	5.	_____
3.	_____	6.	_____

VOCABULARY

1. Is there a **requirement** to drive a car? _____

2. Is your principal an **entertainer**? _____

_____

3. Should you take the **opportunity** to cheat? _____

4. Is Johnny Depp a **celebrity**? _____

5. Do you get a **nomination** when you buy a music CD? _____

_____

6. Is fruit a food **category**? _____

_____

Entertainment Awards

Roll out the red carpet. Polish the trophies. Hear the cries of joy. **Celebrities** *come from cities around the world.* **Entertainers** *get dressed up and come to award shows. People in countries around the world watch the shows on television. Three of the major award shows are the Academy Awards®, Emmy Awards®, and Grammy Awards®.*

The Academy Award® is the Oscar. Oscars recognize excellence in movies. Titanic holds the record for the most awards. In 1997, the movie received 11 Oscars.

The Emmy Awards® recognize excellence in television. There are awards for different **categories**. *There are awards for both primetime and daytime. There are awards for comedies, dramas, and talk shows. Frasier and ER have both been nominated more than 100 times. Friends has received more than 50 Emmy®* **nominations**.

Grammy Awards® recognize excellence in music recording. Carlos Santana and Michael Jackson have each won eight Grammys in one year.

Those are three of the entertainment award shows. What is your favorite award show?

Tasha's Winning Essay

"Are you excited?" asked the woman on the phone.

"Yes," replied Tasha. "I can't believe I won. There were over 1,000 entries."

"Yours was the best! Now, write down the radio station's address," the woman said. "You can come pick up your tickets. There will be extras for your family and one buddy to attend."

Tasha copied the address onto a piece of paper. The essay she wrote qualified her for the radio contest. She won! She was going to the MTV Music Video Awards. Tasha had followed all of the contest's **requirements**. She had to get permission from her mom to enter. She then had to write an essay about why music is an important form of entertainment.

Because her parents are divorced and her mom works long hours, Tasha does not have many **opportunities** to go to big cities and see **celebrities**. Both she and her mother are looking forward to the trip to New York City to see the award show. Tasha wants to see her favorite artists receive their man-on-the-moon trophies. She wonders who will win Best Video of the Year. It is like a dream come true. She can't wait to tell her buddies that she won!

A

1.	boy	legal	excited	music
2.	tall	earn	important	money
3.	kneel	joy	forward	salt
4.	making	shined	woman	graph

B

1. _____ 4. _____

2. _____ 5. _____

3. _____ 6. _____

FLUENCY

C

1.   . . . in countries all over the world. (paragraph 2)

2.   . . . smiling or crying tears of joy. (paragraph 2)

3.   . . . boys know that Dr. Turnbull expects . . . (paragraph 3)

INDEPENDENT READING

Singing Their Way to a Better Life

Harlem is a community in New York. Many of the people who live in Harlem are poor. Gangs and violence are often a part of their daily life.

The Boys Choir of Harlem is making a difference. It offers boys in grades 4 through 12 a way to learn about music and hard work. Dr. Walter Turnbull leads the choir. The choir has 250 members. The Boys Choir of Harlem has entertained people in countries all over the world. They have performed at the White House and have won Grammy Awards. They often leave their audiences smiling or crying tears of joy. Their songs are a mix of classical, jazz, gospel, and pop.

The boys know that Dr. Turnbull expects a lot of them. He emphasizes being a good person. The choir has many rules. The boys go to a private school during the day. They take classes such as history and math. They also take classes in voice and music history. They learn how to play the piano, drums, and bells. The choir members practice in the afternoon after school. Almost all of the boys go on to college after leaving the Boys Choir of Harlem.

PRACTICE AND APPLY

Match each sentence in the left column with the best ending in the right column.

1. You can download		at school or in a car.
2. The entertainer was nominated		for the Hall of Fame.
3. I cannot use my cell phone	the way the clowns joked with each other.	
4. She always cries		and knights of long ago.
5. The crowd enjoyed		music from legal Web sites.
6. I love to read books about queens, kings,	when she watches a sad movie.	

Write a word from the sentences above for each phonics pattern.
*Bonus: Write a second word for each phonics pattern.

7. kn _____ * _____

8. al _____ * _____

9. VCe + ing/ed _____ * _____

10. ph _____ * _____

11. oy _____ * _____

12. y + ed/es _____ * _____

FLUENCY With a partner, take turns reading paragraphs from the Lesson 24 Independent Reading passage. Follow along as your partner reads and check each other for reading errors.

A

1.	write	wrap	wren	wrong
2.	haul	vault	fraud	launch
3.	wreck	wreath	haunt	daunt
4.	dried	stories	knelt	stall

B

1.	buried	often	lived	treasures
2.	excited	pictures	believe	argue
3.	dolphin	important	forward	knight

C

1. _____	4. _____
2. _____	5. _____
3. _____	6. _____

VOCABULARY

ancient	daunting	pharaoh

tomb	mummy	hieroglyphic

The Great Pyramid

*Lanette looked up. Her gaze lifted 480 feet into the air. She was in Giza, Egypt, touring **ancient** Egypt's pyramids. Today she was visiting the Great Pyramid.*

Lanette shook her head in disbelief. She wondered how people could have built the huge structure 5,000 years ago. How did they haul and wrestle the stones into place without modern machines?

*Lanette had read a book about the Great Pyramid. The author explained its size. He hadn't been wrong. The pyramid was amazing. Its size was **daunting**.*

The tour guide explained that the pyramid was made with more than two million heavy stone blocks. Each block weighs at least two tons.

*Inside the pyramid are three burial chambers and several secret passageways. It is believed that the **ancient** Egyptian **pharaoh** ordered the pyramid to be built as his **tomb**.*

*It is likely that the **pharaoh** was indeed buried there with his treasures. However, robbers became quite good at breaking into the pyramids and taking the treasure. Today there is no sign of the **pharaoh** or his treasure.*

Ancient Egypt

People lived in Egypt about 7,000 years ago. The **pharaoh** was the most powerful person in **ancient** Egypt. **Ancient** Egyptians thought of him as a god.

The **ancient** Egyptians believed in life after death. They built **tombs** for the **pharaohs**. They wanted to make sure that they had a good life after death. The **pharaohs** were buried in these **tombs**. The first of these **tombs** were the pyramids. Later **tombs** were built in huge rock structures.

The Egyptians believed the body had to be well cared for. For this reason, Egyptians made **mummies**. Once a **pharaoh** died, his body was dried. The **pharaoh's** body was wrapped in cloth and placed in a coffin. It was believed that the gods would protect the **pharaoh**.

Pharaohs' tombs were filled with treasures and things they would need in the afterlife. There were often paintings on the **tombs**. There was also writing called **hieroglyphics**. A hieroglyph is a picture. Each picture stood for an idea or sound.

In 1922, scientists discovered a **tomb**. Inside they found the **pharaoh** and his treasures. The **mummy** had a mask made of gold. The gold mask and many treasures show how important this **pharaoh** was.

FLUENCY Read the Lesson 26 Independent Reading passage aloud to a small group of students. Read the passage twice.

A

1.	dawn	saw	draw	crawl
2.	jaw	flaw	lawn	hawk
3.	claw	steam	pool	pawn
4.	stay	carries	trail	sights

B

1.	ranger	group	drew	distance
2.	often	buried	lived	treasures
3.	stench	because	flight	again

C

1. _____   4. _____
2. _____   5. _____
3. _____   6. _____

VOCABULARY

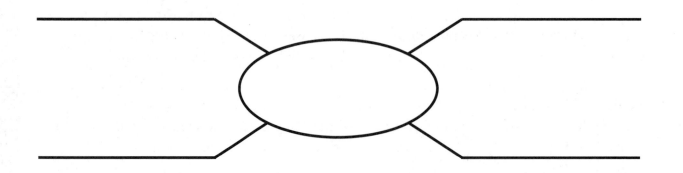

Spraying Hot Water

Nevada is a dry state. Much of its land is desert. However, in one place, water shoots out of the ground. But watch out, it's hot!

*People in Nevada have creative ways of getting water and making electricity. Some people were drilling a well. They were hoping to get water they could use for steam power. What they saw made their jaws drop. They saw a **geyser**. A **geyser** is a spring that repeatedly shoots hot water and steam into the air.*

*The Nevada **geyser** became known as Fly **Geyser**. It is still spewing boiling water out of the ground. Many people think the **geyser** is beautiful. Over the years, the **minerals** in the water and steam have piled up. Today, they are mounds 15 feet high. The water and steam shoots out of the top of the mounds.*

*The colors are amazing at Fly **Geyser**. The mounds are bright red and green. There is a special kind of algae that grows where it is very hot. The Fly **Geyser** is perfect for these plants. The algae give the **geyser** its unique color. People look in **awe** at the Fly **Geyser**.*

Hot Spots in Yellowstone

A group gathered just after dawn at Old Faithful in Yellowstone National Park. "Remember," said the park ranger to the group, "the **geysers**, hot springs, and mud pots are dangerous. Just below the thin ground is boiling water. Keep your distance. Stay on the walkways."

Just then it happened. The famous **geyser** known as Old Faithful began to **erupt**. I wouldn't have believed it if you told me about it, but I saw it with my own eyes. The **eruption** lasted three minutes. Boiling water and steam shot up over 180 feet in the air. It was awesome! The park ranger told us to stick around. The **geyser** would **erupt** again in about 90 minutes. "That is its pattern, 365 days a year," he explained.

Later, I continued my **exploration**. I saw another awesome sight. Crested Pool is deep and hot. When I saw it, the water in the pool was boiling! The bubbles made the water shoot up 10 feet in the air. No one would believe what nature can do!

Yet another sight that inspires **awe** is the Tower Fall. This waterfall plunges 132 feet. I hiked a trail from the top to the bottom. The view was flawless.

I know I will always remember the amazing sights of Yellowstone.

FLUENCY

With a partner, take turns reading paragraphs from the Lesson 27 Independent Reading passage. The first partner reads the first two paragraphs. Then the second partner reads the final three paragraphs. Follow along as your partner reads and check each other for reading errors.

A

1.	landmark	seaside	doghouse	spaceship
2.	highway	bathroom	driveway	backyard
3.	weave	underneath	turned	upside
4.	wrap	shipwreck	served	sight

B

1.	guest	unusual	features	shoe
2.	woman	group	people	ranger
3.	flying	distance	drew	build

C

1. _____	4. _____
2. _____	5. _____
3. _____	6. _____

VOCABULARY

1.  2.  3.  4.

_____   _____   _____   _____

architect   interactive   property   tourist

Inside an Elephant

Some people have ridden on an elephant. There are some people who have been <u>in</u> an elephant—Lucy the elephant building, that is.

*About 100 years ago, a man wanted to sell beachfront **property** in New Jersey. He decided to build a huge elephant-shaped building on the beach. He believed people would come to see the building. They would see the **property** for sale and buy the land. He even got a patent for the elephant-shaped building.*

His plan worked. He built the building and named it Lucy. She stands on the beach, looking outward to the ocean. People came to see Lucy. They entered the doorway in her hind legs. They climbed the staircase. They ate breakfast and lunch high on Lucy's back. They looked at the seaside and the outstanding view from Lucy's back.

*Lucy remains a New Jersey beach **landmark**. **Tourists** still enjoy walking through the elephant-shaped building.*

Unusual Buildings

Architects are people who design buildings. Most buildings have four sides, a roof, doors, and windows. Some **architects** get creative and add unusual features.

Do you remember the nursery rhyme about an old woman who lived in a shoe? One man in Pennsylvania took that nursery rhyme to heart. Mahlon Haines sold shoes. He had a shoe-shaped building designed and built. The building looks like a work boot. It has three bedrooms, two bathrooms, a kitchen, and a living room. Today the shoe house is an ice cream shop and an historic **landmark**. There is even a shoe-shaped doghouse in the backyard.

A company in Ohio sells baskets. They designed and built a building that looks like a huge picnic basket. The windows are in the basket weave.

A family in Tennessee has a house that looks like a flying saucer. Cars park in the driveway underneath the spaceship and a staircase leads up into the bottom of the saucer.

High Point, North Carolina, is known for making furniture. In town is a huge, three-story chest of drawers. Two six-foot long socks hang from one drawer.

Wonder Works is in Florida. It is an **interactive** amusement park. Inside are **exhibits** for your mind. One **exhibit** allows you to feel an earthquake. The Wonder Works building appears to have been turned upside down!

LESSON 29

With a partner, take turns reading paragraphs from the Lesson 28 Independent Reading passage. Follow along as your partner reads and check each other for reading errors.

A

1.	salty	reach	soy	sunlight
2.	writing	phone	maul	skies
3.	cloud	bunnies	ground	knotted
4.	fawn	sprain	stray	whine

B

1.	break	eventually	bridge	permanent
2.	guest	features	treasures	unusual
3.	shoes	landmark	often	highway

C

1.	_____	4.	_____
2.	_____	5.	_____
3.	_____	6.	_____

VOCABULARY

1. erosion
   a. rock making
   b. destroying
   c. wearing away
   d. studying

2. expand
   a. shrink
   b. get bigger
   c. explain
   d. examine

3. formation
   a. melting snow
   b. to build something
   c. size and height
   d. shape of something

4. geology
   a. study of rocks
   b. frost wedging
   c. tall rocks
   d. freezing snow

5. spire
   a. scientist
   b. point or peak
   c. rock layers
   d. natural bridge

 FLUENCY

©Voyager Expanded Learning, L.P.

A Salt Desert

Bolivia is in South America. It is home to a special desert made of salt. When it rains, it becomes a salt lake. A hotel is in the middle of the salt lake. Guess what was used to build the hotel in the salt lake in the salt desert—yes, salt blocks!

A boat is not needed to cross the lake and reach the hotel. In the dry season, visitors walk or drive across the white sand. Salt crystals twinkle in the sunlight. In the wet season, people cross with four-wheeled vehicles. The lake is less than two feet deep at its deepest point.

The salt lake makes a beautiful illusion. On clear days, both the sky and the water are blue. Looking out at the lake, it is almost impossible to tell where the sky ends and the lake begins. The white clouds are reflected in the blue water. Salt **formations** *rise out of the water. They too look like clouds, making the distinction between land and sky even more difficult.*

Rock History

Geology is the study of Earth's rocks, soil, minerals, and history. Many people travel to Utah to study geologic **formations**.

Rainbow Bridge is a bridge made from rock. It is the largest natural bridge in the world. A stream cutting through hard rock formed Rainbow Bridge. It took thousands of years. The bridge is made of **sedimentary rock**. Each layer of rock is a different color. The colors are most vivid in the afternoon sunlight.

Bryce Canyon National Park teaches another lesson in **geology**. One geologic **formation** found at Bryce is a hoodoo. Hoodoos are tall, skinny **spires** of rock. These awesome rock **formations** can be as tall as a 10-story building.

A hoodoo is formed by **erosion**. One form of **erosion** that shapes hoodoos is frost wedging. It snows on a rock. The snow thaws. The melted water works its way into cracks in the rock. Then the water freezes again. Freezing water **expands**, or gets bigger. When it **expands**, the rock cracks. Eventually, pieces of the rock break off. Over time, a tall **spire** is left where the rock was. Rain also causes **erosion**. The rain washes away parts of the rock.

It takes thousands of years to form a hoodoo. But the **erosion** that creates the hoodoos also destroys them. Over 100 years, between two and four feet of a hoodoo are eroded away.

A

1.	squeal	thirst	point	break
2.	wharf	because	eventually	music
3.	permanent	shores	southeast	argue
4.	bridge	sunset	joy	graph

B

1. _____ **4.** _____

2. _____ **5.** _____

3. _____ **6.** _____

C

1. . . . receive sunlight from dawn to dusk. (paragraph 2)

2. . . . begin work on Jefferson all over. (paragraph 4)

3. . . . filled with awe as they look . . . (paragraph 5)

INDEPENDENT READING

An American Symbol

Most people recognize the Statue of Liberty as a symbol of our country. Mount Rushmore is another symbol.

Mount Rushmore is a mountain in South Dakota. A group of people, including Gutzon Borglum, had an idea. They wanted to carve faces into a mountain. They chose Mount Rushmore because it faced southeast. That meant it would receive sunlight from dawn to dusk. It was also made of a rock that would not erode quickly.

Borglum decided to carve the faces of George Washington, Thomas Jefferson, Theodore Roosevelt, and Abraham Lincoln. Before Borglum could begin carving, tons of rock were blasted off the mountain. What was left was smooth rock.

Borglum went to work on Washington. He started by carving an egg shape. Then he added eyes and other facial features. Next, Borglum began working on Jefferson. After two years, the rock cracked. Borglum had to begin work on Jefferson all over again.

Carving the monument took 14 years. Today, tourists are filled with awe as they look at the great presidents. Mount Rushmore is a symbol of America's courage, freedom, dreams, and greatness.

PRACTICE AND APPLY

Read each of the following groups of ideas about the passages you have read. Circle the main idea in each group.

Lesson 26: The Great Pyramid
1. Lanette discovered a mummy and his treasures.
2. Lanette read a book about the Great Pyramid.
3. Lanette was a tourist at the Great Pyramid.

Lesson 27: Hot Spots in Yellowstone
1. The author saw Old Faithful.
2. The author was in awe of the sights in Yellowstone.
3. A geyser shoots hot water and steam in the air.

Lesson 28: Unusual Buildings
1. There is unique architecture in America.
2. Architects are people who design buildings.
3. A company in Ohio built an office in the shape of a picnic basket.

Lesson 29: Rock History
1. Unusual rock formations are found in Utah.
2. Rainbow Bridge is a natural bridge made of rock.
3. Erosion causes the formation of a hoodoo.

Lesson 30: An American Symbol
1. The bald eagle and Statue of Liberty are symbols of our country.
2. Tons of rock was blasted off of the mountain.
3. The faces of four presidents were carved into the rocks of Mount Rushmore.